SUPER DiaPeR BABY 2
THE Invasion of the POTTY SnatcherS

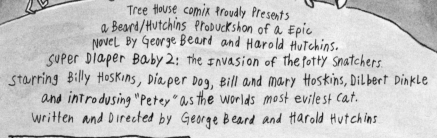

D0012155

Tree House comix proudly Presents
a Beard/Hutchins Produckshon of a Epic
Novel By George Beard and Harold Hutchins.
SuPer Diaper Baby 2: the Invasion of the Potty Snatchers.
Starring Billy Hoskins, Diaper Dog, Bill and mary Hoskins, Dilbert Dinkle
and introdusing "Petey" as the worlds most evilest cat.
written and Directed by George Beard and Harold Hutchins

Scholastic Inc.
New York Toronto London Auckland
Sydney Mexico City New Delhi Hong Kong

this novel
has been
rated:

TA
Totally AWESOME!!!
Some material may be too
Awesome for Boring old grown-ups

For Madison Mancini

No part of this publication may be reproduced, stored in a retrieval system, or transmitted in any form or by any means, electronic, mechanical, photocopying, recording, or otherwise, without written permission of the publisher. For information regarding permission, please write to: Permissions Department, Scholastic Inc., 557 Broadway, New York, NY 10012.

This book was originally published in hardcover by the Blue Sky Press in 2011.

ISBN 978-0-545-17533-3 (Trade) / ISBN 978-0-545-38580-0 (BC)

Be sure to check out Dav Pilkey's Extra-Crunchy Web Site O' Fun at www.pilkey.com.

12 11 10 9 8 7 6   14 15 16/0

Printed in the United States of America   40
First printing, September 2011

It was the story of a baby who acksidently fell into some super power juice.

Splash

He drank it and got super powers and stuff.

Also, a dog drank the juice.

Glug glug

He became super powery, too!

The baby and the dog are best friends now and they live together with their mom and dad.

They both wear diapers too!

one time a evil guy tried to steal Super Diaper Babys powers...

This is going to be sweet!

Transfer Helmet

...but he made a boo-boo and got Turned into poo-poo!

Hey!

Transfer Helmet

Then he got some New clear waste on him and he grew way bigger and eviler!!!

Rar!

New clear power plant

So Super Diaper Baby and Diaper Dog flew into action!

We'll get you Deputy Doo-Doo!

nuh-uh!!!

They grabbed a big Roll of toilet paper from on top of a bilding...

BOB'S TOILET Paper compeny

HEY NO Fair!

BOB

...wrapped up Deputy Doo-Doo...

...and Left him where all doo-doo belongs!

WELCOME TO URANUS

Hooray for super Diaper Baby and Diaper Dog!

Chapters

15

FLiP·O·RAMA

HEres How it works!!!!

STEP 1
PLace your Left hand inside the dotted Lines marked "LEFt Hand Here". HoLd The Book open FLat.

STEP 2
GRasp the Right-hand Page with YOUR Right thumb and index finger (inside The dotted Lines marked Right ThumB Here").

STEP 3
NOW QUiCKLY FLip The Right-hand Page back and fourTh UntiL the PitCher appears To Be Animated!

(for extra fun, try adding Your own sound Afecks).

17

FLIP-O-RAMA #1

(pages 19 and 21)

Remember, Flip only page 19. While you are flipping, be shure you can see the pitcher on page 19 And the one on page 21.

IF you Flip Quickly, The two pitchers will start to look like one Animated pitcher.

Dont forget to add your own Sound Afecks!

Left Hand Here

Down Goes the Airplane...

Right Thumb Here

Up Goes the Airplane...

FLiP-O-RAMA 2

Remember --- FLip ONLY page 23. While you are flipping, be shure you can see the pitcher on page 23 and the one on page 25.

If you flip Quickly, The Two pitchers will start To Look Like one animated pitcher.

Dont forget Those sound afecks!

Left Hand Here

Down go the airplane

Right
Thumb
Here

Up go the airplane

29

30

31

32

33

34

35

36

38

39

40

42

43

44

45

47

48

49

53

FLIP·O·RAMA 3

If you forgot how to do this already, please see your doctor. Afterwards, Turn to page 17 for further instruckshons

Left Hand Here.

Drinking Dr. Dinkle

55

Right Thumb Here.

Drinking Dr. Dinkle

58

59

60

Snatcher Catchers

63

Right Thumb Here

Snatcher catchers

Jacker Smackers

Right
Thumb
Here

Jacker Smackers

Cheater Beaters!

Right
thumb
Here

Cheater Beaters!

76

77

78

79

80

81

82

83

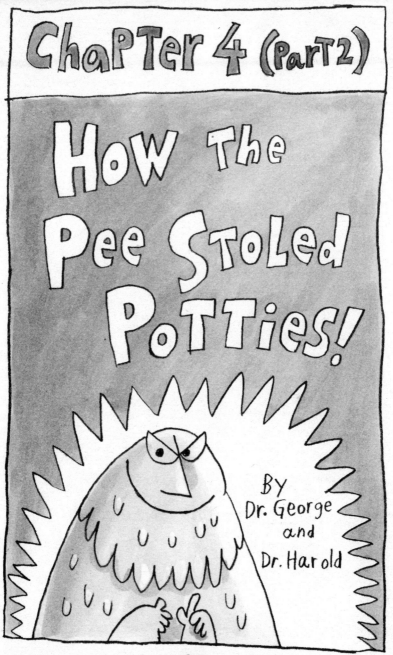

That Night Rip Van Tinkle
was frowning a frown,
as he sneered at the houses
below in the town.

No one Knows why he was
feeling so ruthless...
It could be because all his
money was useless.

Or maybe because he was
just feeling cranky.
Or possibly cuz his bad breath
was so stanky.
But we think the very best
reason might be
that he smelled like a bucket
of twelve-day-old pee.

But whatever the reason
    his stank or his dough,
he stood up there hating
    the people below.
He snarled as he frowned
    feeling drearier and drearier.
"Those Jerks in the city
Think Theyr'e So Superier!

"They all be hatin'!
But heres what I think:
I think things would change
if <u>they</u> started to stink!

If all of those idiots
smelled just like pee,
they wouldent be goin' Round
disrespectin' me!!!"

89

And Then Rip Van Tinkle
  Thought up a idea.
  But we couldent Think up
  a rhyme for "idea."

"I Know just what to do"
  he sTarted professin'.
"I'LL teach all of those good-
  Smelling people a Lessen!"

91

So he Took some scrap metal
and used an old wheel
To build a contrapshon
with Teeth made of steel.

He hammered its tail
and sharpened its claws,
and welded its wiskers
and titened its Jaws.

93

It took 24 hours
   From when he'd begun,
'Till the Robo-Kitty
   Three Thousand was done.
"ALL I need is a driver.
   I need someone mean.
I need someone evil ♥
   to run my machine".

So he took his cat "Petey"
   and strapped him in tight...

...Then both of those villens sneaked out in the night.

"Watch this," Rip Van Tinkle said
Laffing out Loud...
and soon he began to
turn into a cloud.

And when the pee cloud
was over the town,
the thunderclaps crashed
and the pee drops rained down.

Into the chimneys
the pee drops they flew
And they entered each house
Knowing Just what To do.

98

Each drop found a wrench...

... and each wrench found a bolt...

JOLT

... and soon every Toilet popped up with a JOLT!

They carried each toilet
  Right out of each house, and
Into the jaws of the
  Kitty Three thousend.

Crunch! Crunch! went the robot
without too much trouble
and soon every potty
was crushed into rubbel!

But in one little house,
on one little street,
One drip heard the sounds
of two little feet.

The pee drop looked up
and what did it see?
but a cute little tot
with a fluffy blankie.

The baby looked down
and said, "MR. Pee, Hey!
Why are you taking
our toilet away?"

And that mean little drip,
do you know what it did?
why, it made up a lie
and it said to the kid:

"Your toilet is broken---
   it squeaks when you flush it.
I'll take it away and I'll
   clean it and brush it.

I'll shine it right up
   —I'll fix it and oil it,
and soon I'll return with a
   Good-as-new toilet."

And the baby believed what
the pee drop had said.
So it got him a juice box
and took him to bed.

BiLLyS
Room

And at last when the baby
was sleeping and dreaming,
that nasty old pee drop
went on with its skeeming!

He carried the Toilet
  Right out the door.
and once it was crushed,
  He went back to get more.

The snatching of Potties
went on through the night,
And into the dawn of the
Mornings first Light.

And once every toilet
was crushed by the cat,
The people awoke and cried,
"What up wit' dat?"

"Our toilets are gone!
Weve got to go potty!
Oh, we do not like this!
Oh, no we do notty!"

So they each crossed their legs
and squirmed all around,
And they squeezed and they clenched,
and they bobbed up and down.

'Till all of the people
were doing "Pee dances"
shouting, "Someone please help us,
or we'll wet our pantses!"

113

They wiggled all morning
   in torment and Trauma,
Just like they're doing
   in this Flip-o-Rama →

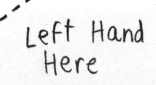

Left Hand
Here

Pee-Dance
RevoLushon

Right
Thumb
Here

Pee-Dance
RevoLushon

Soon, warm Liquid Streams
with Yellowish Hues
Flowed down their Legs
and filled up their Shoes.

And they sobbed as they stood
in their puddles of piddle,
But no one could help them.
Not even a Little.

CHAPTER 5

the Aftermath

120

121

122

123

124

126

127

129

130

131

133

134

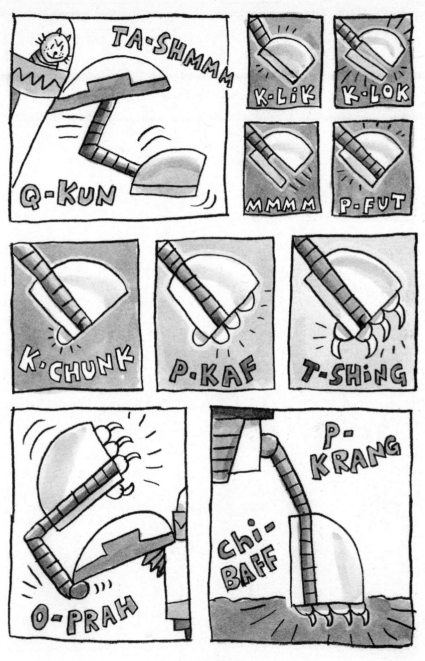

135

136

137

138

139

141

Koo-Koo For Kitty Nip!

143

Right thumb Here

Koo-Koo For Kitty Nip!

FLIP·O·RAMA

Left Hand
Here

KiTTY FOR KOO-KOO NiP!

Right
thumb
Here.

KiTTY FOR KOO-KOO NiP!

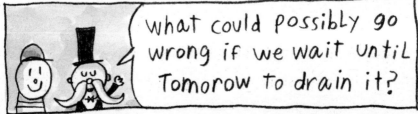

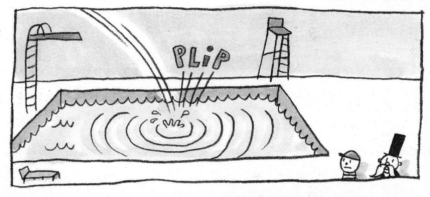

154

157

158

160

161

FLiP·O·RAMA

Left Hand Here

Building Basher

163

Right thumb Here

Building Basher

166

169

172

175

176

AND SO
I'm a Big, evil ice monster...
...And I'm gonna destroy the WorLd!!!

179

180

181

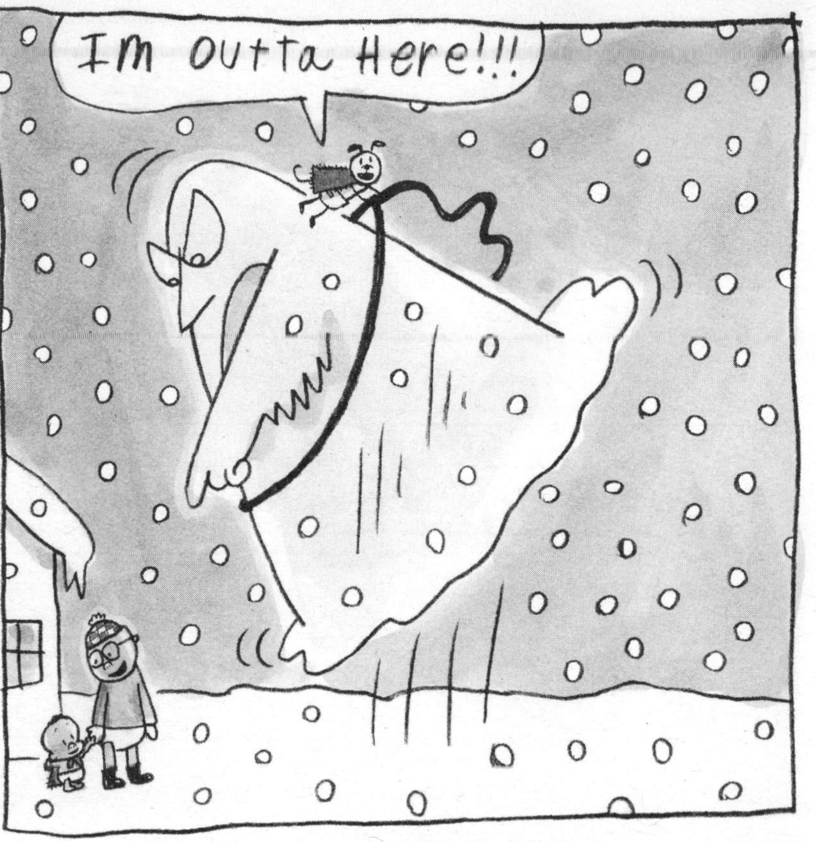
I'm outta Here!!!

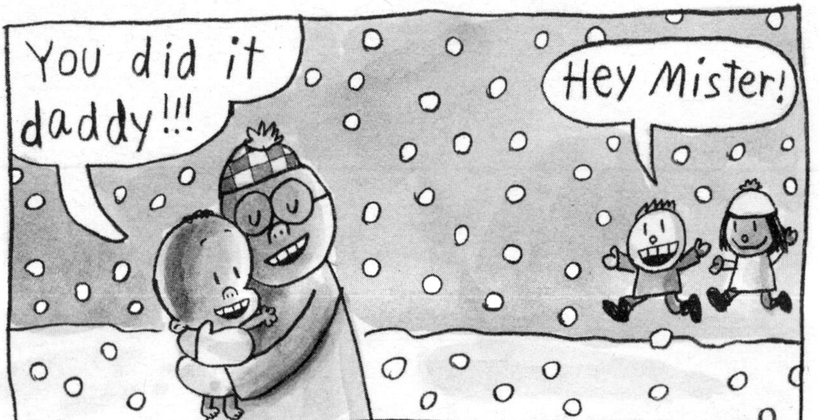
You did it daddy!!!
Hey Mister!

183

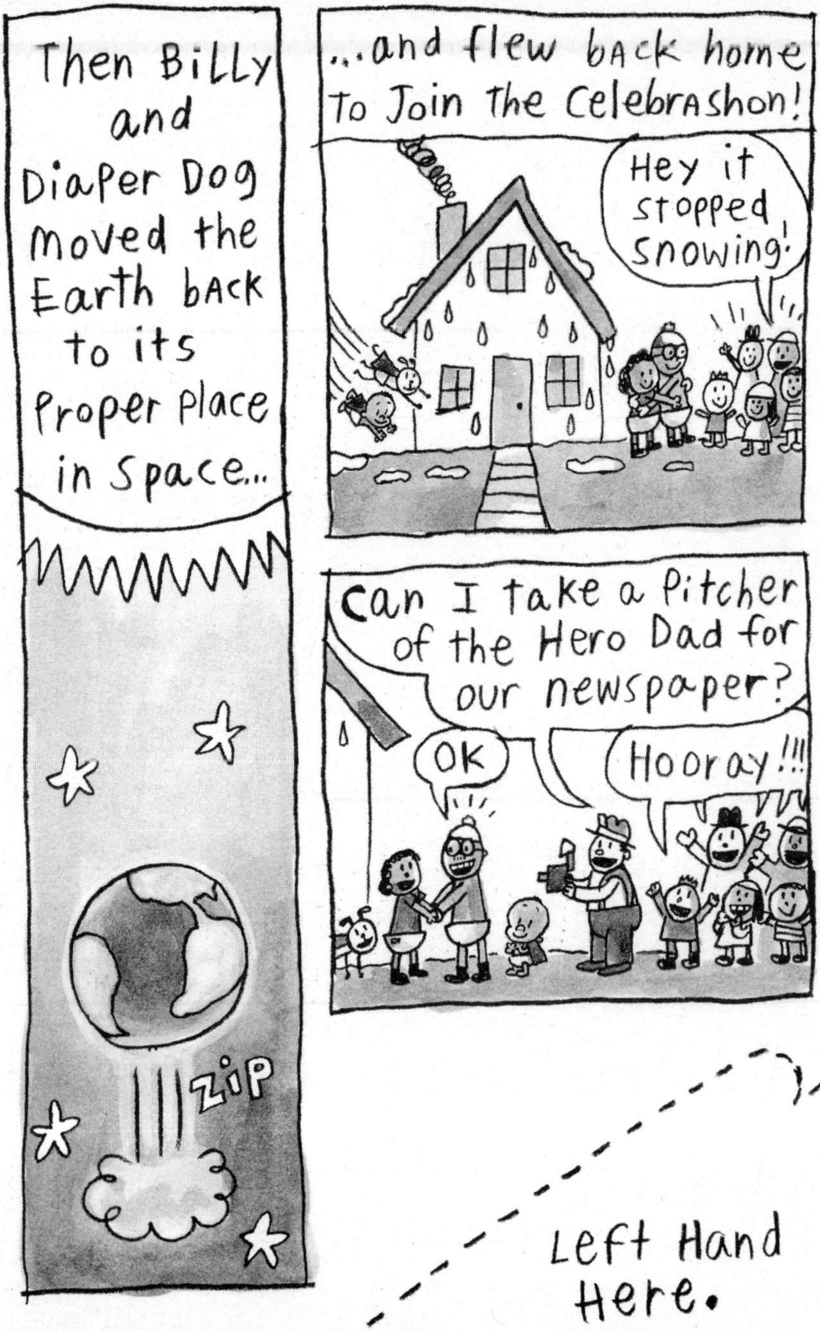

Left Hand Here.

Say Cheese!!!

Right
thumb
Here

Say Cheese!!!